CLASSIC JAZZ FOR FLUTE

WISE PUBLICATIONS
LONDON/NEW YORK/PARIS/SYDNEY/COPENHAGEN/BERLIN/MADRID/TOKYO

C000081660

EXCLUSIVE DISTRIBUTORS:
MUSIC SALES LIMITED
8/9 FRITH STREET, LONDON W1D 3JB, ENGLAND.
MUSIC SALES PTY LIMITED
120 ROTHSCHILD AVENUE, ROSEBERY, NSW 2018, AUSTRALIA.

THIS BOOK © COPYRIGHT 1997, 2002 BY WISE PUBLICATIONS.
ORDER NO. AM937057
ISBN 0-7119-5756-8

COMPILED BY PETER EVANS.
MUSIC ARRANGED BY JACK LONG.
MUSIC PROCESSED BY ENIGMA MUSIC PRODUCTION SERVICES & SETON MUSIC GRAPHICS.
PRINTED IN THE UNITED KINGDOM.

YOUR GUARANTEE OF QUALITY
AS PUBLISHERS, WE STRIVE TO PRODUCE EVERY BOOK
TO THE HIGHEST COMMERCIAL STANDARDS.
THIS BOOK HAS BEEN CAREFULLY DESIGNED TO MINIMISE AWKWARD
PAGE TURNS AND TO MAKE PLAYING FROM IT A REAL PLEASURE.
PARTICULAR CARE HAS BEEN GIVEN TO SPECIFYING ACID-FREE, NEUTRAL-SIZED PAPER
MADE FROM PULPS WHICH HAVE NOT BEEN ELEMENTAL CHLORINE BLEACHED.
THIS PULP IS FROM FARMED SUSTAINABLE FORESTS AND WAS PRODUCED WITH SPECIAL
REGARD FOR THE ENVIRONMENT. THROUGHOUT, THE PRINTING AND BINDING HAVE BEEN
PLANNED TO ENSURE A STURDY, ATTRACTIVE PUBLICATION WHICH SHOULD GIVE YEARS OF ENJOYMENT.
IF YOUR COPY FAILS TO MEET OUR HIGH STANDARDS, PLEASE INFORM US AND
WE WILL GLADLY REPLACE IT.

www.musicsales.com

Fingering Chart

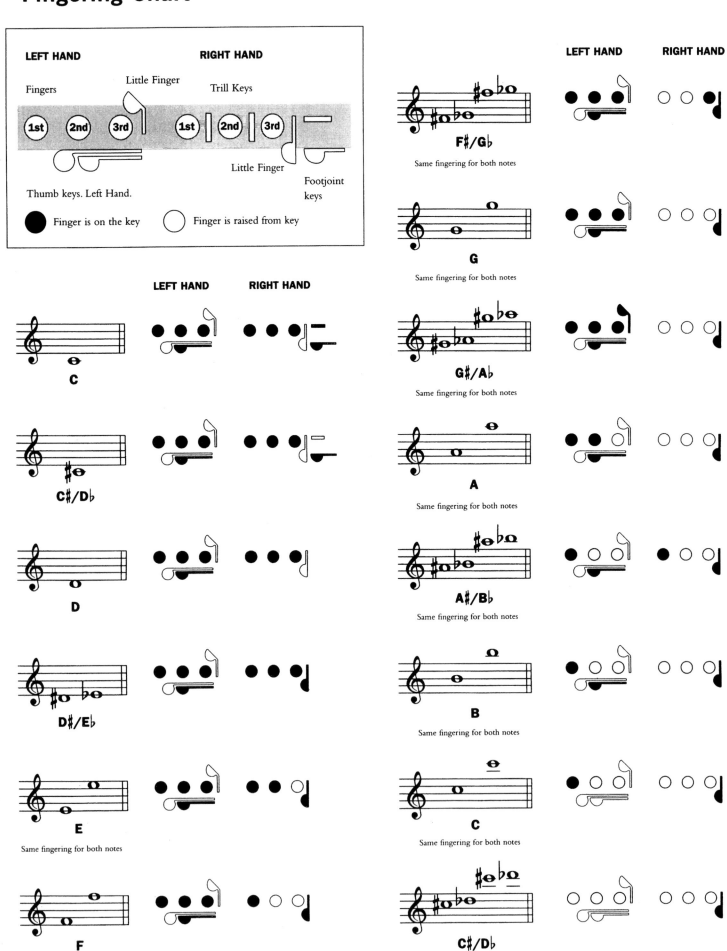

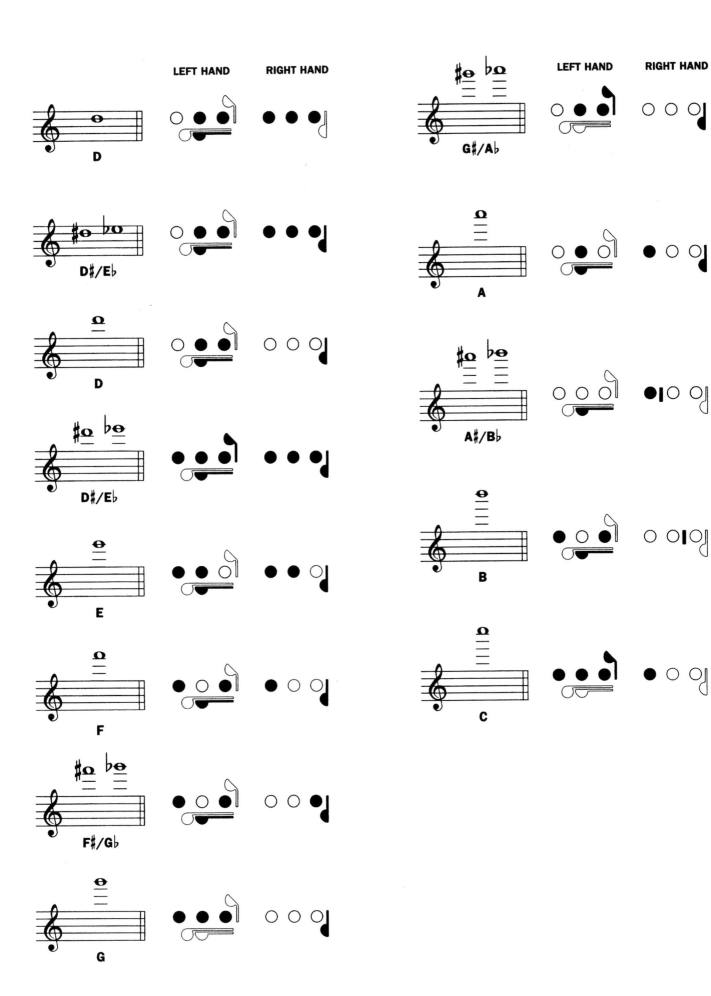

A NIGHT IN TUNISIA

MUSIC BY FRANK PAPARELLI & JOHN 'DIZZY' GILLESPIE
WORDS BY RAYMOND LEVEEN

Medium fast

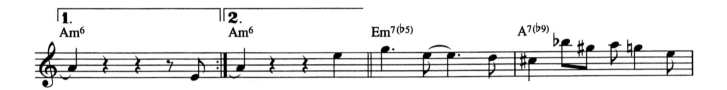

AIN'T MISBEHAVIN'

WORDS BY ANDY RAZAF
MUSIC BY THOMAS WALLER & HARRY BROOKS
© COPYRIGHT 1929 MILLS MUSIC INCORPORATED, USA.
LAWRENCE WRIGHT MUSIC COMPANY LIMITED, LONDON WC2 & REDWOOD MUSIC LIMITED, LONDON NW1.

BABY WON'T YOU PLEASE COME HOME

WORDS & MUSIC BY CHARLES WARFIELD & CLARENCE WILLIAMS

Medium bounce

BARK FOR BARKSDALE

BY GERRY MULLIGAN

BERNIE'S TUNE

BY BERNIE MILLER
© COPYRIGHT 1954 RENEWED 1982 ATLANTIC MUSIC CORPORATION, USA.
SUB-PUBLISHED IN THE UK & EIRE BY MARADA MUSIC LIMITED, ADMINISTERED BY GLOBAL MUSIC LIMITED, 171 SOUTHGATE ROAD, LONDON N1.
ALL RIGHTS RESERVED. INTERNATIONAL COPYRIGHT SECURED.

BLUES IN THE NIGHT (MY MAMA DONE TOL' ME)

WORDS BY JOHNNY MERCER
MUSIC BY HAROLD ARLEN

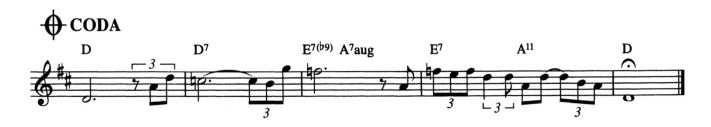

BLUESETTE

WORDS BY NORMAN GIMBEL
MUSIC BY JEAN THIELEMANS

Bright jazz waltz

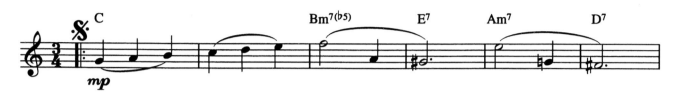

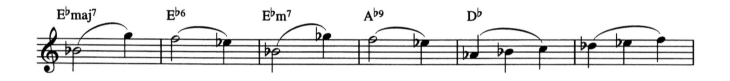

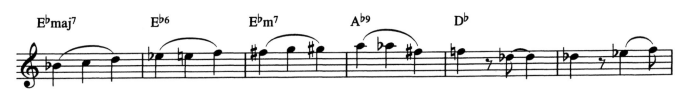

CODA

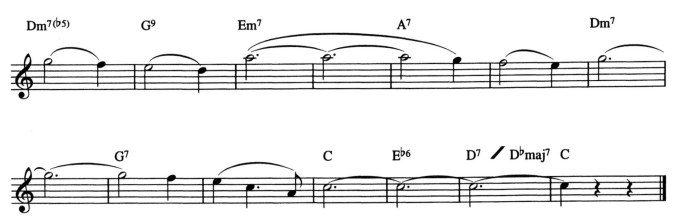

BOOGIE WOOGIE BUGLE BOY

WORDS & MUSIC BY DON RAYE & HUGHIE PRINCE
© COPYRIGHT 1940, 1941 MCA MUSIC (A DIVISION OF MCA INCORPORATED, USA).
© COPYRIGHT RENEWED 1967, 1968 AND ASSIGNED TO MCA MUSIC (A DIVISION OF MCA INCORPORATED, USA).
MCA MUSIC LIMITED, 77 FULHAM PALACE ROAD, LONDON W6 FOR THE WORLD (EXCLUDING NORTH, SOUTH AND CENTRAL AMERICA, JAPAN, AUSTRALASIA AND THE PHILIPPINES).
ALL RIGHTS RESERVED. INTERNATIONAL COPYRIGHT SECURED.

Medium Boogie Woogie

BIG NOISE FROM WINNETKA

WORDS BY GIL RODIN & BOB CROSBY
MUSIC BY BOB HAGGART & RAY BAUDAC
© COPYRIGHT 1940 BREGMAN, VOCCO AND CONN INCORPORATED, USA.
AUTHORISED FOR SALE IN THE UNITED KINGDOM BY PERMISSION OF BOOSEY & HAWKES MUSIC PUBLISHERS LIMITED, LONDON W1.

CARAVAN

BY DUKE ELLINGTON, IRVING MILLS & JUAN TIZOL

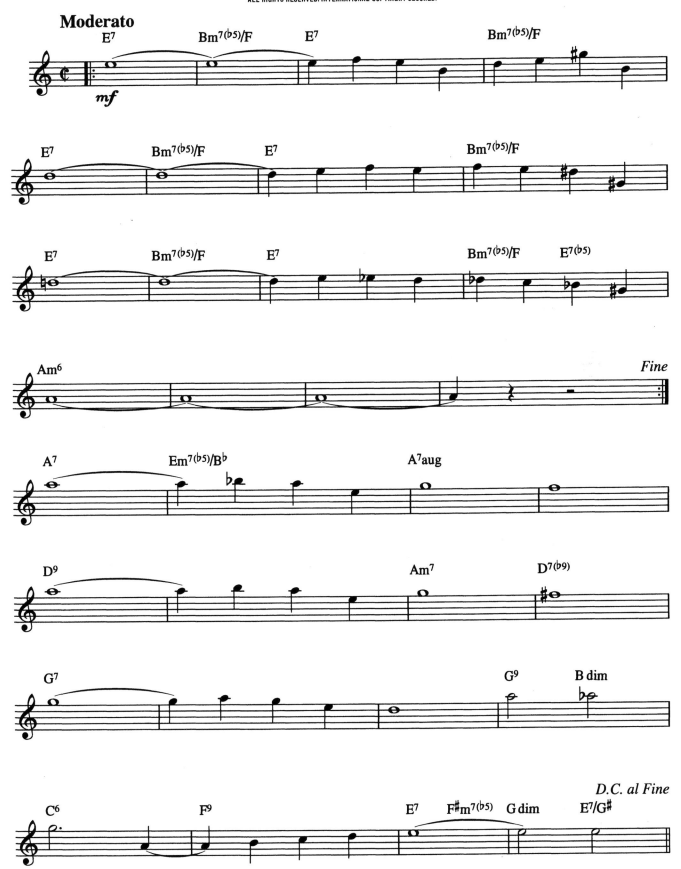

COME FLY WITH ME

LYRICS BY SAMMY CAHN
MUSIC BY JAMES VAN HEUSEN

CHELSEA BRIDGE

BY BILLY STRAYHORN
© COPYRIGHT 1942 TEMPO MUSIC INCORPORATED, USA.
CAMPBELL CONNELLY & COMPANY LIMITED, 8/9 FRITH STREET, LONDON W1.
ALL RIGHTS RESERVED. INTERNATIONAL COPYRIGHT SECURED.

CRY ME A RIVER

WORDS & MUSIC BY ARTHUR HAMILTON
© COPYRIGHT 1955 CHAPPELL & COMPANY INCORPORATED, USA.
WARNER CHAPPELL MUSIC LIMITED, 129 PARK STREET, LONDON W1.
ALL RIGHTS RESERVED. INTERNATIONAL COPYRIGHT SECURED.

CUTE

WORDS BY STANLEY STYNE
MUSIC BY NEAL HEFTI
© COPYRIGHT 1958 NEAL HEFTI MUSIC INCORPORATED, USA.
CINEPHONIC MUSIC COMPANY LIMITED, 8/9 FRITH STREET, LONDON W1.

Moderato

DON'T GET AROUND MUCH ANYMORE

WORDS BY BOB RUSSELL
MUSIC BY DUKE ELLINGTON

DON'T DREAM OF ANYBODY BUT ME
(LI'L DARLIN')

WORDS BY BART HOWARD
MUSIC BY NEAL HEFTI

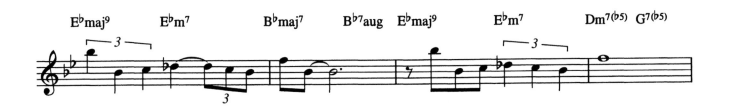

CODA

EAST OF THE SUN (AND WEST OF THE MOON)

WORDS & MUSIC BY BROOKS BOWMAN

FASCINATING RHYTHM

MUSIC & LYRICS BY GEORGE GERSHWIN & IRA GERSHWIN
© COPYRIGHT 1924 (RENEWED) CHAPPELL & COMPANY AND NEW WORLD MUSIC COMPANY LIMITED, ADMINISTERED BY WB MUSIC CORPORATION, USA.
THIS ARRANGEMENT © COPYRIGHT 1996 CHAPPELL & COMPANY AND NEW WORLD MUSIC COMPANY LIMITED, ADMINISTERED BY WB MUSIC CORPORATION, USA.
WARNER CHAPPELL MUSIC LIMITED, 129 PARK STREET, LONDON W1.
ALL RIGHTS RESERVED. INTERNATIONAL COPYRIGHT SECURED.

GEORGIA ON MY MIND

WORDS BY STUART GORRELL
MUSIC BY HOAGY CARMICHAEL

FLY ME TO THE MOON (IN OTHER WORDS)

WORDS & MUSIC BY BART HOWARD
© COPYRIGHT 1954, 1962, 1973 BY ALMANAC MUSIC INCORPORATED, NEW YORK, USA.
ASSIGNED TO TRO ESSEX MUSIC LIMITED, SUITE 2.07, PLAZA 535 KINGS ROAD, LONDON SW10 FOR THE WORLD (EXCLUDING CANADA AND USA).
ALL RIGHTS RESERVED. INTERNATIONAL COPYRIGHT SECURED.

Moderato

HERE'S THAT RAINY DAY

WORDS & MUSIC BY JOHNNY BURKE & JIMMY VAN HEUSEN
© COPYRIGHT 1953 BURKE & VAN HEUSEN INCORPORATED.
ALL RIGHTS ASSIGNED TO BOURNE COMPANY & DORSEY BROTHERS MUSIC INCORPORATED.
WARNER CHAPPELL MUSIC LIMITED, 129 PARK STREET, LONDON W1 (50%)/CAMPBELL CONNELLY & COMPANY LIMITED, 8/9 FRITH STREET, LONDON W1 (50%).
ALL RIGHTS RESERVED. INTERNATIONAL COPYRIGHT SECURED.

HONEYSUCKLE ROSE

MUSIC BY THOMAS 'FATS' WALLER
WORDS BY ANDY RAZAF
© COPYRIGHT 1929 SANTLY BROTHERS INCORPORATED, USA.
CAMPBELL CONNELLY & COMPANY LIMITED, 8/9 FRITH STREET, LONDON W1 (50%)/REDWOOD MUSIC LIMITED, IRON BRIDGE HOUSE, 3 BRIDGE APPROACH, LONDON N1 (50%).
ALL RIGHTS RESERVED. INTERNATIONAL COPYRIGHT SECURED.

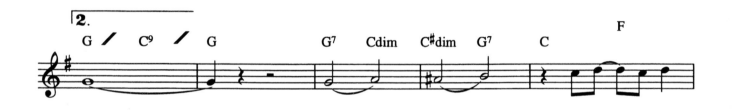

HOW INSENSITIVE

MUSIC BY ANTONIO CARLOS JOBIM
ORIGINAL LYRICS BY VINICIUS DE MORAES. ENGLISH LYRICS BY NORMAN GIMBEL
© COPYRIGHT 1963, 1964 BY ANTONIO CARLOS JOBIM AND VINICIUS DE MORAES, BRAZIL.
MCA MUSIC LIMITED, 77 FULHAM PALACE ROAD, LONDON W6 FOR THE BRITISH COMMONWEALTH (EXCLUDING CANADA), SOUTH AFRICA, CONTINENT OF EUROPE
(EXCLUDING ITALY, FRANCE, ITS COLONIES, PROTECTORATES AND MANDATED TERRITORIES, ALGERIA, TUNISIA, MOROCCO, ANDORRA AND MONACO),
ALL RIGHTS RESERVED. INTERNATIONAL COPYRIGHT SECURED.

I'LL REMEMBER APRIL

WORDS & MUSIC BY DON RAYE, GENE DE PAUL & PATRICIA JOHNSON
© COPYRIGHT 1942 MCA MUSIC (A DIVISION OF MCA INCORPORATED, USA).
MCA MUSIC LIMITED, 77 FULHAM PALACE ROAD, LONDON W6 FOR THE WORLD (EXCLUDING NORTH, SOUTH AND CENTRAL AMERICA, JAPAN, AUSTRALASIA AND THE PHILIPPINES).

I'M BEGINNING TO SEE THE LIGHT

WORDS & MUSIC BY HARRY JAMES, DUKE ELLINGTON, JOHNNY HODGES & DON GEORGE
© COPYRIGHT 1944 GRAND MUSIC CORPORATION, USA.
CAMPBELL CONNELLY & COMPANY LIMITED, 8/9 FRITH STREET, LONDON W1.
ALL RIGHTS RESERVED. INTERNATIONAL COPYRIGHT SECURED.

I'M GETTIN' SENTIMENTAL OVER YOU

WORDS BY NED WASHINGTON
MUSIC BY GEO. BASSMAN
© COPYRIGHT 1933 LAWRENCE MUSIC PUBLISHERS INCORPORATED, USA.
© COPYRIGHT ASSIGNED 1934 MILLS MUSIC INCORPORATED, USA.
DASH MUSIC COMPANY LIMITED, 8/9 FRITH STREET, LONDON W1.
ALL RIGHTS RESERVED. INTERNATIONAL COPYRIGHT SECURED.

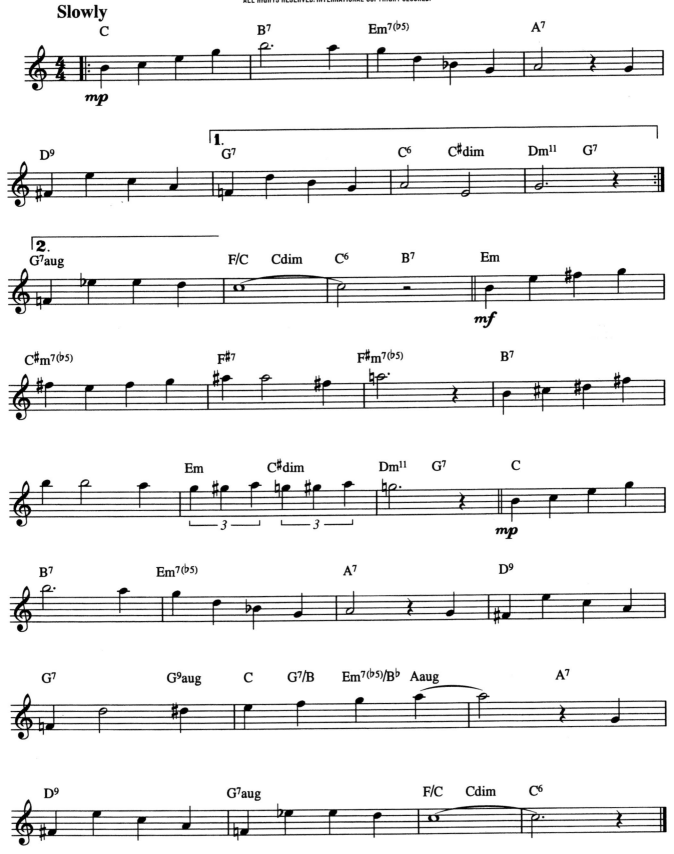

I WISH I KNEW HOW IT WOULD FEEL TO BE FREE

WORDS BY BILLY TAYLOR & DICK DALLAS
MUSIC BY BILLY TAYLOR

Medium 'Rock' tempo

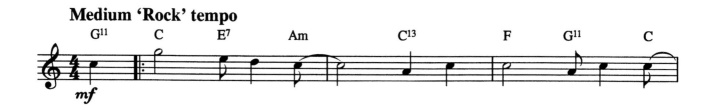

IN A SENTIMENTAL MOOD

WORDS & MUSIC BY DUKE ELLINGTON, IRVING MILLS & MANNY KURTZ
© COPYRIGHT 1935 BY AMERICAN ACADEMY OF MUSIC INCORPORATED, NEW YORK, USA.
REPUBLISHED CONTAINING NEW COPYRIGHT MATTER 1935 BY AMERICAN ACADEMY OF MUSIC INCORPORATED.
SOLE AGENTS FOR THE BRITISH EMPIRE (EXCLUDING CANADA) AND EUROPE, J.R. LAFLEUR AND SON LIMITED.
AUTHORISED FOR SALE IN GREAT BRITAIN AND NORTHERN IRELAND ONLY BY PERMISSION OF BOOSEY & HAWKES MUSIC PUBLISHERS LIMITED.
ALL RIGHTS RESERVED. INTERNATIONAL COPYRIGHT SECURED.

IT'S A RAGGY WALTZ

MUSIC BY DAVE BRUBECK

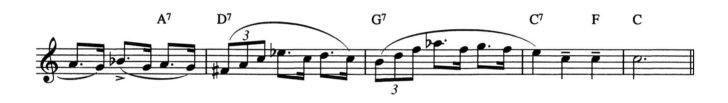

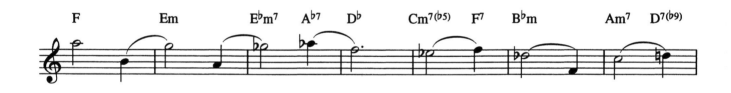

IT DON'T MEAN A THING
(IF IT AIN'T GOT THAT SWING)

WORDS BY IRVING MILLS
MUSIC BY DUKE ELLINGTON

LAZY RIVER

WORDS & MUSIC BY HOAGY CARMICHAEL & SIDNEY ARODIN
© COPYRIGHT 1931 BY PEER INTERNATIONAL CORPORATION. COPYRIGHT RENEWED 1958 BY PEER INTERNATIONAL CORPORATION, USA.
PEERMUSIC (UK) LIMITED, 8-14 VERULAM STREET, LONDON WC1X 8LZ.

Moderato

LEARNIN' THE BLUES

WORDS & MUSIC BY DOLORES VICKI SILVERS
© COPYRIGHT 1955 BARTON MUSIC CORPORATION, USA.
THE INTERNATIONAL MUSIC NETWORK LIMITED, INDEPENDENT HOUSE, 54 LARKSHALL ROAD, CHINGFORD, LONDON E4 6PD.
ALL RIGHTS RESERVED. INTERNATIONAL COPYRIGHT SECURED.

Medium swing

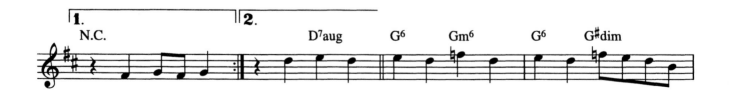

LAZYBONES

WORDS & MUSIC BY JOHNNY MERCER & HOAGY CARMICHAEL
© COPYRIGHT 1933 BY SOUTHERN MUSIC PUBLISHING COMPANY INCORPORATED, USA.
LAWRENCE WRIGHT MUSIC COMPANY LIMITED, LONDON W1 FOR GREAT BRITAIN, IRELAND AND COLONIES, (EXCLUDING CANADA AND AUSTRALASIA)
BUT INCLUDING THE CONTINENT OF EUROPE EXCEPTING LATIN COUNTRIES AND SWITZERLAND.
ALL RIGHTS RESERVED. INTERNATIONAL COPYRIGHT SECURED.

Slow Blues

LULLABY OF BIRDLAND

MUSIC BY GEORGE SHEARING
WORDS BY GEORGE DAVID WEISS
© COPYRIGHT 1952, 1953 & 1954 LONGITUDE MUSIC COMPANY, USA.
WINDSWEPT PACIFIC MUSIC LIMITED, 27 QUEENSDALE PLACE, LONDON W11 4SQ (85%).
ALL RIGHTS RESERVED. INTERNATIONAL COPYRIGHT SECURED.

MEAN TO ME

WORDS & MUSIC BY ROY TURK & FRED E. AHLERT
© COPYRIGHT 1929 COPYRIGHT RENEWED 1957. REVERTED AND ASSIGNED TO PENCIL MARK MUSIC INCORPORATED/FRED AHLERT MUSIC CORPORATION, USA.
MEMORY LANE MUSIC LIMITED, RONDOR MUSIC (LONDON) LIMITED/BURTON WAY MUSIC LIMITED AND REDWOOD MUSIC LIMITED, LONDON. UNITED KINGDOM COPYRIGHT OWNERS.
ALL RIGHTS RESERVED. INTERNATIONAL COPYRIGHT SECURED.

MEDITATION (MEDITAÇAO)

ORIGINAL WORDS BY NEWTON MENDONCA. ENGLISH LYRIC BY NORMAN GIMBEL. MUSIC BY ANTONIO CARLOS JOBIM

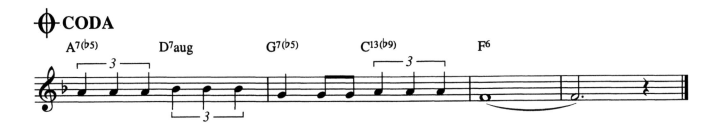

MIDNIGHT SUN

WORDS BY JOHNNY MERCER
MUSIC BY SONNY BURKE & LIONEL HAMPTON

Moderato

MOOD INDIGO

WORDS & MUSIC BY DUKE ELLINGTON, IRVING MILLS & ALBANY BIGARD
© COPYRIGHT 1931 BY GOTHAM MUSIC SERVICE INCORPORATED, NEW YORK, USA.
FOR GREAT BRITAIN, IRELAND AND COLONIES (EXCLUDING CANADA AND AUSTRALASIA)
THE PROPERTY OF LAWRENCE WRIGHT MUSIC COMPANY LIMITED, 127 CHARING CROSS ROAD, LONDON WC2.
ALL RIGHTS RESERVED. INTERNATIONAL COPYRIGHT SECURED.

MERCY, MERCY, MERCY

WORDS BY GAIL FISHER LEVY & VINCENT LEVY
MUSIC BY JOSEF ZAWINUL
© COPYRIGHT 1966, 1967 ZAWINUL MUSIC, A DIVISION OF GOPAM ENTERPRISES INCORPORATED.
JEWEL MUSIC PUBLISHING COMPANY LIMITED, 22 DENMARK STREET, LONDON WC2.
ALL RIGHTS RESERVED. INTERNATIONAL COPYRIGHT SECURED.

Medium slow 'Rock'

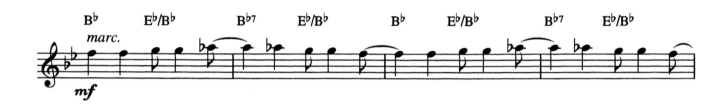

MOONGLOW

WORDS & MUSIC BY WILL HUDSON, EDDIE DE LANGE & IRVING MILLS
© COPYRIGHT 1934 EXCLUSIVE PUBLICATIONS INCORPORATED, USA.
COPYRIGHT ASSIGNED 1934 TO MILLS MUSIC INCORPORATED, USA.
AUTHORISED FOR SALE IN THE UK AND EIRE ONLY BY PERMISSION OF BOOSEY & HAWKES MUSIC PUBLISHERS LIMITED, LONDON.
ALL RIGHTS RESERVED. INTERNATIONAL COPYRIGHT SECURED.

ONE NOTE SAMBA (SAMBA DE UMA NOTA SO)

ORIGINAL WORDS BY N. MENDONCA. ENGLISH LYRIC BY JON HENDRICKS. MUSIC BY ANTONIO CARLOS JOBIM
© COPYRIGHT 1961,1962,1964 ANTONIO CARLOS JOBIM AND MRS N MENDONCA, BRAZIL.
MCA MUSIC LIMITED, 77 FULHAM PALACE ROAD, LONDON W6 FOR THE BRITISH COMMONWEALTH (EXCLUDING CANADA).
ALL RIGHTS RESERVED. INTERNATIONAL COPYRIGHT SECURED.

OPUS ONE

ORNITHOLOGY

BY CHARLIE PARKER & BENNY HARRIS
© COPYRIGHT 1946 RENEWED 1974 ATLANTIC MUSIC CORPORATION, USA.
SUB-PUBLISHED IN THE UK & EIRE BY MARADA MUSIC LIMITED, ADMINISTERED BY GLOBAL MUSIC LIMITED, 171 SOUTHGATE ROAD, LONDON N1.
ALL RIGHTS RESERVED. INTERNATIONAL COPYRIGHT SECURED.

PERDIDO

MUSIC BY JUAN TIZOL
WORDS BY HARRY LENK AND ERVIN DRAKE
© COPYRIGHT 1942 TEMPO MUSIC INCORPORATED, USA.
CAMPBELL CONNELLY & COMPANY LIMITED, 8/9 FRITH STREET, LONDON W1.
ALL RIGHTS RESERVED. INTERNATIONAL COPYRIGHT SECURED.

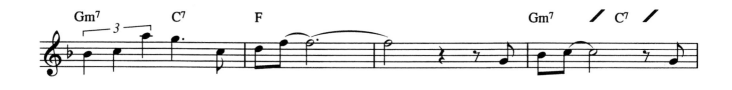

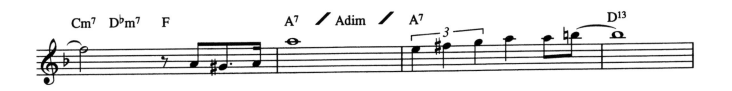

PETITE FLEUR (LITTLE FLOWER)

WORDS & MUSIC BY SIDNEY BECHET
© COPYRIGHT 1952 AND 1959 LES EDITIONS MUSICALES DU CARROUSEL, FRANCE.
TRO-ESSEX MUSIC LIMITED, SUITE 2.07, PLAZA 535 KINGS ROAD, LONDON SW10.

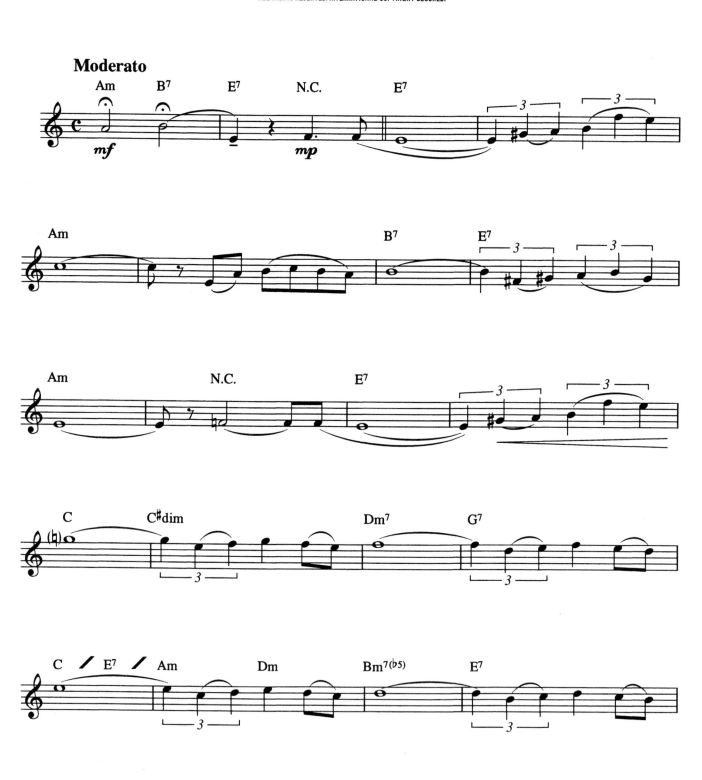

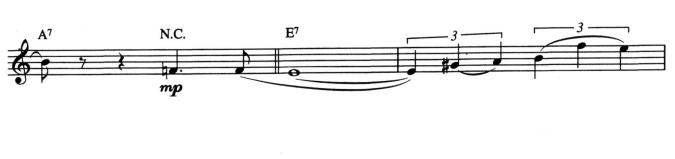

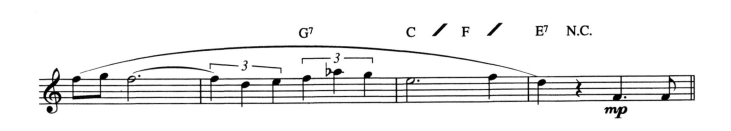

RECADO BOSSA NOVA (THE GIFT)

WORDS & MUSIC BY DJALMA FERREIRA & LUIZ ANTONIO
© COPYRIGHT 1959, 1963 RYTVOC INCORPORATED, USA.
TRO-ESSEX MUSIC LIMITED, SUITE 2.07, PLAZA 535 KINGS ROAD, LONDON SW10.
ALL RIGHTS RESERVED. INTERNATIONAL COPYRIGHT SECURED.

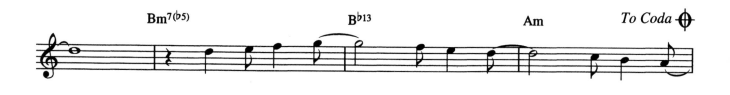

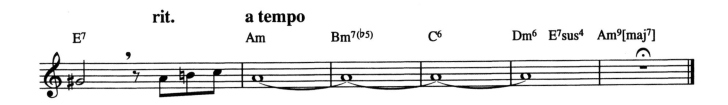

ROUND MIDNIGHT

BY COOTIE WILLIAMS & THELONIOUS MONK
© COPYRIGHT 1944 BY ADVANCED MUSIC CORPORATION, USA.
WARNER CHAPPELL MUSIC LIMITED, 129 PARK STREET, LONDON W1.
ALL RIGHTS RESERVED. INTERNATIONAL COPYRIGHT SECURED.

Slow '2'

QUIET NIGHTS OF QUIET STARS (CORCOVADO)

ENGLISH WORDS BY GENE LEES
MUSIC & ORIGINAL WORDS BY ANTONIO CARLOS JOBIM
© COPYRIGHT 1962,1965 BY ANTONIO CARLOS JOBIM, BRAZIL.
MCA MUSIC LIMITED, 77 FULHAM PALACE ROAD, LONDON W6 FOR THE BRITISH COMMONWEALTH (EXCLUDING CANADA & SOUTH AFRICA).
ALL RIGHTS RESERVED. INTERNATIONAL COPYRIGHT SECURED.

SATIN DOLL

WORDS BY JOHNNY MERCER
MUSIC BY DUKE ELLINGTON & BILLY STRAYHORN
© COPYRIGHT 1953 & 1960 BY TEMPO MUSIC INCORPORATED, USA.
CAMPBELL CONNELLY & COMPANY LIMITED, 8/9 FRITH STREET, LONDON W1.

Moderato

SLIGHTLY OUT OF TUNE (DESAFINADO)

ENGLISH LYRIC BY JON HENDRICKS & JESSIE CAVANAUGH
MUSIC BY ANTONIO CARLOS JOBIM

STARS FELL ON ALABAMA

WORDS BY MITCHELL PARISH
MUSIC BY FRANK PERKINS

SWEET SUE - JUST YOU

WORDS BY WILL J. HARRIS
MUSIC BY VICTOR YOUNG
© COPYRIGHT 1928, 1956 SHAPIRO BERNSTEIN & COMPANY INCORPORATED, USA.
THIS ARRANGEMENT COPYRIGHT 1996 SHAPIRO BERNSTEIN & COMPANY INCORPORATED, USA.
CAMPBELL CONNELLY & COMPANY LIMITED, 8/9 FRITH STREET, LONDON W1.
ALL RIGHTS RESERVED. INTERNATIONAL COPYRIGHT SECURED.

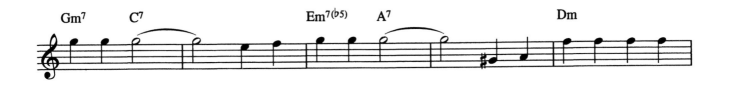

T'AINT WHAT YOU DO
(IT'S THE WAY THAT CHA DO IT)

WORDS & MUSIC BY SY OLIVER & JAMES YOUNG
© COPYRIGHT 1939 MCA MUSIC (A DIVISION OF MCA INCORPORATED, USA).
MCA MUSIC LIMITED, 77 FULHAM PALACE ROAD, LONDON W6 FOR THE WORLD
(EXCLUDING SOUTH AND CENTRAL AMERICA, JAPAN, AUSTRALASIA AND THE PHILIPPINES).
ALL RIGHTS RESERVED. INTERNATIONAL COPYRIGHT SECURED.

Moderato

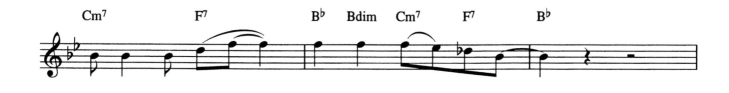

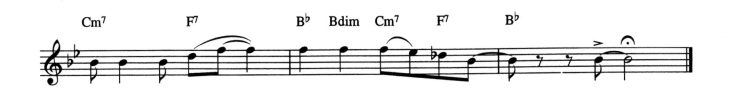

TAKE FIVE

BY PAUL DESMOND
© COPYRIGHT 1960 AND 1961 BY DERRY MUSIC COMPANY, USA. CONTROLLED BY VALENTINE MUSIC GROUP LIMITED FOR THE WORLD
(EXCLUDING USA, CANADA, JAPAN, GERMANY, AUSTRIA, AUSTRALASIA, SCANDINAVIA, FINLAND, ICELAND, FRANCE, BENELUX, ITALY, REPUBLIC OF SOUTH AFRICA AND RHODESIA).
ALL RIGHTS RESERVED. INTERNATIONAL COPYRIGHT SECURED.

Moderato

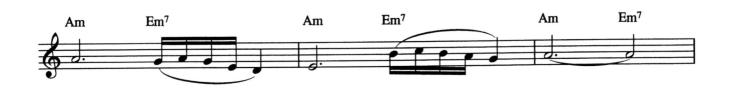

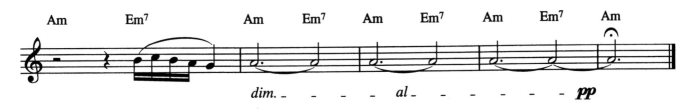

TAKE THE 'A' TRAIN

WORDS & MUSIC BY BILLY STRAYHORN

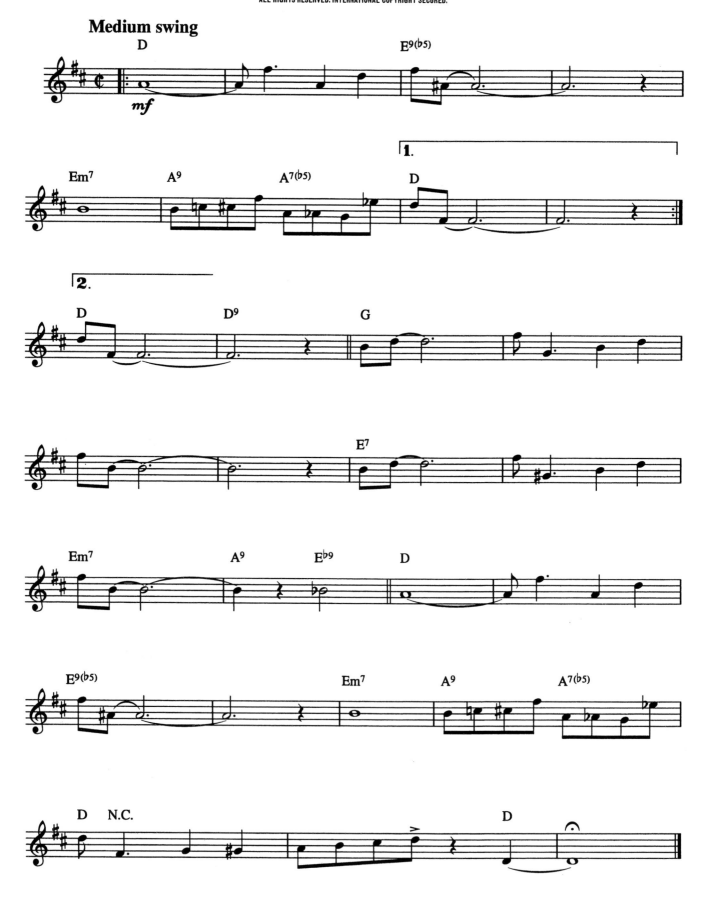

THE BEST IS YET TO COME

WORDS BY CAROLYN LEIGH
MUSIC BY CY COLEMAN

THE GIRL FROM IPANEMA (GAROTA DE IPANEMA)

ORIGINAL WORDS BY VINICIUS DE MORAES. ENGLISH LYRIC BY NORMAN GIMBEL. MUSIC BY ANTONIO CARLOS JOBIM
© COPYRIGHT 1963 ANTONIO CARLOS JOBIM AND VINICIUS DE MORAES, BRAZIL.
MCA MUSIC LIMITED, 77 FULHAM PALACE ROAD, LONDON W6 FOR THE BRITISH COMMONWEALTH
(EXCLUDING CANADA) SOUTH AFRICA, EIRE, GERMANY, AUSTRIA, SWITZERLAND, FRANCE AND ITALY.
ALL RIGHTS RESERVED. INTERNATIONAL COPYRIGHT SECURED.

THE LONESOME ROAD

WORDS BY GENE AUSTIN
MUSIC BY NATHANIEL SHILKRET

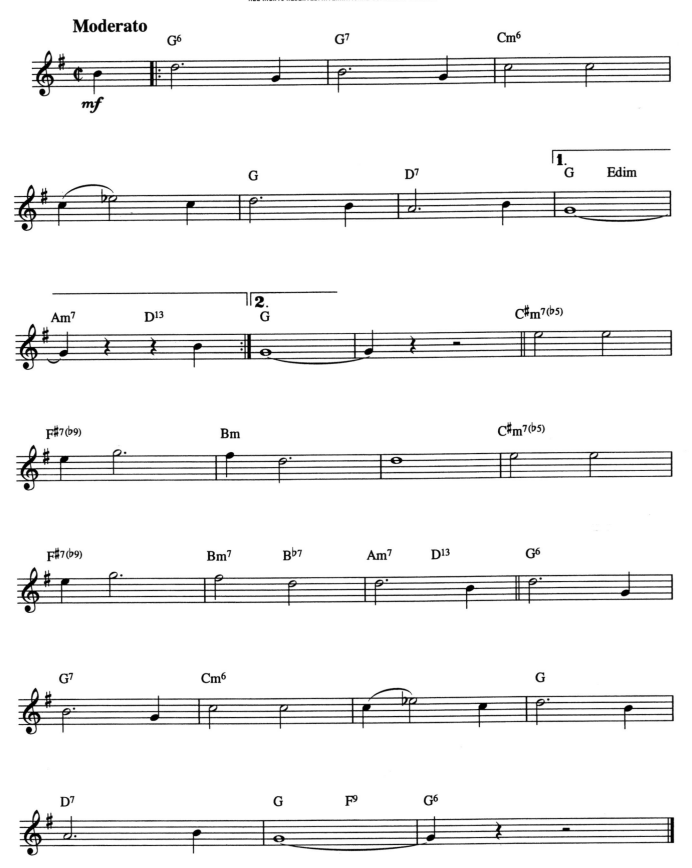

THE MOOD I'M IN

WORDS & MUSIC BY PETE KING & PAUL FRANCIS WEBSTER
© COPYRIGHT 1964 LEEDS MUSIC CORPORATION, USA.
CAMPBELL CONNELLY & COMPANY LIMITED, 8/9 FRITH STREET, LONDON W1.

THE VERY THOUGHT OF YOU

WORDS & MUSIC BY RAY NOBLE

Moderato

TUXEDO JUNCTION

WORDS BY BUDDY FEYNE
MUSIC BY ERSKINE HAWKINS, WILLIAM JOHNSON & JULIAN DASH
© COPYRIGHT 1940 LEWIS MUSIC PUBLISHING COMPANY INCORPORATED, USA.
AUTHORISED FOR SALE IN THE UNITED KINGDOM OF GREAT BRITAIN AND NORTHERN IRELAND ONLY BY PERMISSION OF BOOSEY & HAWKES MUSIC PUBLISHERS LIMITED.
ALL RIGHTS RESERVED. INTERNATIONAL COPYRIGHT SECURED.

Medium swing

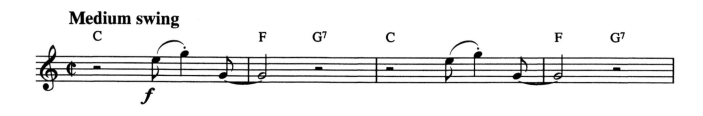

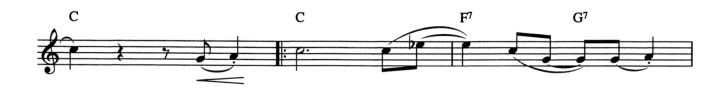

UNDECIDED

WORDS BY SID ROBIN
MUSIC BY CHARLES SHAVERS
© COPYRIGHT 1939,1954 BY LEEDS MUSIC CORPORATION (ASSIGNED TO MCA MUSIC, NEW YORK, USA).
MCA MUSIC LIMITED, 77 FULHAM PALACE ROAD, LONDON W6 FOR THE WORLD
(EXCLUDING NORTH, CENTRAL AND SOUTH AMERICA, JAPAN, AUSTRALASIA, AND THE PHILLIPPINES).
ALL RIGHTS RESERVED. INTERNATIONAL COPYRIGHT SECURED.

Bright swing

WALKIN' SHOES

BY GERRY MULLIGAN

WALTZ FOR DEBBY

MUSIC BY BILL EVANS
WORDS BY GENE LEES

CODA

WAVE

WORDS & MUSIC BY ANTONIO CARLOS JOBIM

Bossa nova

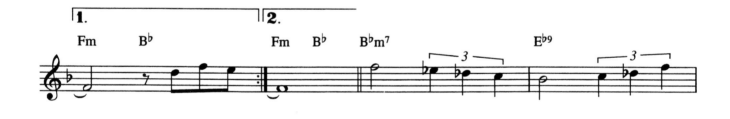

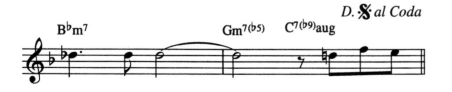

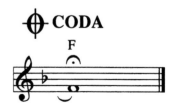

YARDBIRD SUITE

BY CHARLIE PARKER
© COPYRIGHT 1946 RENEWED 1974 ATLANTIC MUSIC CORPORATION, USA.
SUB-PUBLISHED IN THE UK & EIRE BY MARADA MUSIC LIMITED, ADMINISTERED BY GLOBAL MUSIC LIMITED, 171 SOUTHGATE ROAD, LONDON N1.
ALL RIGHTS RESERVED. INTERNATIONAL COPYRIGHT SECURED.